new wom...

collection

— Randy crawf...

Wise Publications

London / New York / Paris / Sydney / Copenhagen / Berlin / Madrid / Tokyo

Exclusive distributors:
Music Sales Limited
8/9 Frith Street, London W1D 3JB, England.
Music Sales Pty Limited
120 Rothschild Avenue, Rosebery, NSW 2018, Australia.

Order No. AM974787
ISBN 0-7119-9542-7
This book © Copyright 2002 by Wise Publications.

Front cover main photograph courtesy of Getty Images.
All other photographs courtesy of LFI.

Your Guarantee of Quality:

As publishers, we strive to produce every book
to the highest commercial standards.

While endeavouring to retain the original running
order of the recorded album, the book has been
carefully designed to minimise awkward page turns
and to make playing from it a real pleasure.

Particular care has been given to specifying
acid-free, neutral-sized paper made from pulps which
have not been elemental chlorine bleached.

This pulp is from farmed sustainable forests and
was produced with special regard for the environment.

Throughout, the printing and binding have been
planned to ensure a sturdy, attractive publication
which should give years of enjoyment.

If your copy fails to meet our high standards,
please inform us and we will gladly replace it.

Printed in Malta by Interprint Limited.

www.musicsales.com

ain't it funny

Words & Music by Jennifer Lopez & Cory Rooney

1. It seemed to be like the per-fect thing for you and me.
(Verse 2 see block lyric)

strange when you're feel - ing things you should - n't feel,_ oh I wish this could_ be real._____ Ain't it

fun - ny how a mo - ment could just change your life,_ and you don't want to face what's wrong or right._Ain't it

1.

strange how fate can play a part_ in the sto - ry of your heart.

2.

sto - ry of your heart.

I locked a - way my heart, but you just set it free, e - mo - tions I felt

Verse 2:
Sometimes I think that a true love can never be
I just believe that somehow it wasn't meant for me.
Life can be cruel in a way that I can't explain
And I don't think that I could face it all again.
I barely know you but somehow I know what you're about
A deeper love I've found in you and I no longer doubt
You've touched my heart and it altered every plan I've made
And now I feel that I don't have to be afraid.

angel

Words & Music by Sarah McLachlan

arms of_____ the an - gel, fly a - way_____ from here._____

From this dark, cold_____ ho - tel room   and the

end - less - ness that you__ fear.   You are pulled from the

wreck - age   of your si - lent___ re - ve - rie._____ You're in the

arms of _____ the an - gel, may you find _____ some com - fort _____ here. _____

2. So tired of the _____ here. _____

You're in the arms of _____ the

11

Verse 2:
So tired of the straight line
And everywhere you turn
There's vultures and thieves at your back
And the storm keeps on twisting
You keep on building the lies
That you make up for all that you lack
It don't make no difference
Escape one last time
It's easier to believe
In this sweet madness
Oh this glorious sadness
That brings me to my knees.

In the arms of the angel   *etc.*

beauty on the fire

Words & Music by Natalie Imbruglia, Gary Clark & Matthew Wilder

Verse 2:
Here it comes again
You raise the bar even higher
I cannot catch my breath
So throw the beauty on the fire
Don't push too hard
Limitation scars.

Tonight could I be lost forever   *etc.*

by your side

Words by Sade Adu
Music by Sade Adu, Stuart Matthewman, Andrew Hale & Paul Spencer Denman

D.%. al Coda

can't get you out of my head

Words & Music by Cathy Dennis & Rob Davis

Verse 2:
There's a dark secret in me
Don't leave me locked in your heart
Set me free *etc.*

don't know why

Words & Music by Jesse Harris

Verse 3:
Out across the endless sea
I will die in ecstasy
But I'll be a bag of bones
Driving down the road alone.

My heart is drenched in wine etc.

Verse 4:
Something has to make you run
I don't know why I didn't come
My field is empty as a drum
I don't know why I didn't come
I don't know why I didn't come
I don't know why I didn't come

don't need the sun to shine
(to make me smile)

Words & Music by Gabrielle & Jonathan Shorten

And though the rain may fall, no, I won't care at all 'cause
ba - by, I know that I got you.

Repeat ad lib. to fade

Verse 2:
Every day there's a change
You bring out the best in me
My inner soul is what you know
That is how you speak to me
You seem to understand
You know just who I am
And baby, this is how I feel.

Don't need the sun to shine   *etc.*

emotion

Words & Music by Barry Gibb & Robin Gibb

words of a bro - ken heart it's just e - mo - tion_____ caught up in sor-

- row, lost__ in my soul._____ But if you don't come__ back, come home to me dar-

- ling,___ no - bo - dy left in this world to hold me tight, no - bo - dy to hold

(2nd time)

me   in this world to kiss good - night,   no - bo - dy____ to kiss____ me._____

Good   ni - - - - ight.

Verse 2:
I'm there at your side,
I'm part of all the things you are
But you've got a part of someone else
You've got to go find your shining star

And where are you now   *etc.*

eternal flame

Words & Music by Billy Steinberg, Tom Kelly & Susanna Hoffs

-ing? Do you un-der-stand?___ Do you feel the same___ or am I on-ly

dream - ing? Is this burn-ing an e - ter-nal flame?

2. I be-lieve___ it's meant to___ be___ dar-ling,___ I watch you when_ you are sleep-

-ing, you be-long with me.___ Do you feel the same___ or am I on-ly

48

family affair

Words & Music by Mary J. Blige, Bruce Miller, Andre Young, Camara Kambon, Mike Elizondo,
Melvin Bradford, Asiah Louis & Luchana Lodge

Let's get it crunk, we gon' have fun up on it in this dan - ce - rie. We got ya'll op - en now you're

float - in' so you gots to dance for me. Don't need no ha - ter - a - tion, hol - ler - a - tion, in this dance - ce -

- rie. Let's get it per - cu - lat - ing while you're wait - ing, so just dance for

me. 1. Come on ev - 'ry bo - dy get on__ up,__ 'cause you know we gots to get it crunk.

(Verse 2 see block lyric)

float-in' so you gots to dance for me. Don't need no ha-ter-a-tion, hol-ler-a-tion, in this dance-ce-

1.
-rie. Let's get it per-cu-lat-ing while you're wait-ing, so just dance for

2.
while you're wait-ing, so just dance for

me.__ Don't need no ha-ters.__ We're just try-ing to love one a-no-ther. We just

want y'all to have a good time, no more dra-ma in your life. Work real hard to make a dime, if ya got

Verse 2:
It's only gonna be about a matter of time
Before you get loose and start to lose your mind
Cop you a drink, go 'head and rock your ice
'Cause we celebrating No More Drama in our life
With a great track pumpin', everybody's jumpin'
Go ahead and twist your back and get your body bumpin'
I told you leave your situations at the door
So grab somebody and get your ass on the dance floor.

Let's get it crunk, we gon' have fun up on it *etc.*

fields of gold

Words & Music by Sting

that I've bro - ken. But I swear in the days still left we will walk in fields of gold. We'll walk in fields of gold. Ooh. Ma - ny

59

freak like me

Words & Music by Gary Numan, Eugene Hanes, Marc Valentine, Loren Hill,
William Collins, George Clinton & Gary Cooper

rough - neck bro - ther that can sa - tis - fy me.___ (Just for me.)___ If___ you are___

that kind__ of man__ 'cause I'm__ that kind__ of girl,___ I've got a

frea - ky sec - ret ev - 'ry - bo - dy__ sing 'cause we don't give a damn a - bout a thing. 'Cause I will be a

Verse 2:
Boy you're moving kind of slow
You gotta keep it up now there you go
That's just one thing that a man must do
I'm packing all the flavours you need
I got you shook up on your knees
'Cause it's all about the dog in me.

I wanna freak in the morning *etc.*

get over you

Words & Music by Rob Davies, Henri Korpi, Mathias Johansson, Nina Woodford & Sophie Ellis-Bextor

Ay yi yi ya._ Ay yi yi ya._ Ay yi yi ya._ Ay yi yi ya._

Ai yi yi ya._ Ai yi yi ya._ Ai yi yi ya._

Ai yi yi ya._ 1. You think you've got your way but ba-by there's a catch, don't
(Verse 2 see block lyrics)

Verse 2:
I let you have your say
You never compromised
Complaining every day
About everything in sight
I'd let you stay awhile
And now I'm getting bored
No substance in your style
And you're not the man you thought.

You had me taken in etc.

how come you don't call me

Words & Music by Prince

Verse 2:
Still light the fire on the rainy night
Still like it better when you're holding me tight
Everybody said
Everybody said that we should never part
Tell me baby, baby, baby why
Why you wanna go and break my heart.

All I wanna know baby *etc.*

kiss kiss

Words & Music by Aksu Sezen, Juliette Jaimes & Steve Welton-Jaimes

Mm!

Mm!   1. When you look at me, tell me what you see. This is what you get, it's the way I am.
(Verse 2 see block lyric)

Verse 2:

You could be mine baby, what's your star sign
Won't you take a step into the lions den
I can hear my conscience calling me, calling me
Say I'm gonna be a bad girl again
Why don't you come on over, we can't leave this all undone
Got a devil on my shoulder, there's no place for you to run.

You don't have to act   *etc.*

lately

Words & Music by Willie Baker, Pete Woodruff & Chris Kelly

83

sit - tin' a - way_ watch - ing the days_ go by._____

Ba - by I've been torn a - part,_ I wish you had - n't broke my heart,_ I'm

miss - ing you babe,_ miss - ing you ev - 'ry day._

Late - ly I've been torn a - part,_ I wish you had - n't broke my heart,_ I'm

miss - ing you babe,_ miss - ing you ev - 'ry day.___

Late - ly been think-ing 'bout you ba - by, just sit-tin' a-way_ watch-ing the days_ go by.__

Late - ly___ been think - ing 'bout you ba - by, just

sit - tin' a - way_ watch - ing the days_ go by.___

i'm not a girl, not yet a woman

Words & Music by Max Martin, Rami & Dido

1. I used to think

(Verse 2 see block lyric)

I had the ans-wers to ev-'ry-thing.___ But now I know___

Verse 2:
I'm not a girl
There is no need to protect me
It's time that I, learn to face up to this
On my own
I've seen so much more than you know now
So don't tell me to shut my eyes.

I'm not a girl *etc.*

move this mountain

Words & Music by Sophie Ellis-Bextor, Stephan James & Ben Hillier

1. What do you want from me?___ I stand be-fore_ you, no_ at-tempt to__ leave.
(Verse 2 see block lyric)

I'm too tired to dis-a-gree,___ I

Verse 2:
Come and take the rest of me
I never thought I wouldn't want you near
This is all I'll ever be
I understand you look around to see this dawning.

Oh, do you know *etc.*

my life

Words & Music by Dido Armstrong, Rollo Armstrong & Mark Bates

Verse 2:
Oh, the world has sat in the palm of my hand
Not that you'd see
And I'm tired and bored of waiting for you
And all those things you never do.

Cos it's me and my life *etc.*

a new day has come

Words & Music by Aldo Nova & Stephan Moccio

D.%. al Coda

Ooh. _____ Let the

⊕ Coda

has _____ come.

Repeat ad lib. to fade

Oh. _____ Ah. _____

Verse 3:
Where it was dark, now there's light
Where there was pain now there's joy
Where there was weakness I've found my strength
All in the eyes of a boy.

Hush now *etc.*

one day in your life

Words & Music by Anastacia, Sam Watters & Louis Biancaniello

one day i'll fly away

Words by Will Jennings
Music by Joe Sample

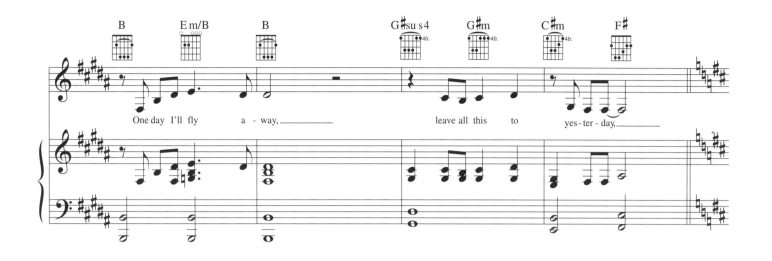

One day I'll fly a - way, _____ leave all this to yes - ter - day, _____

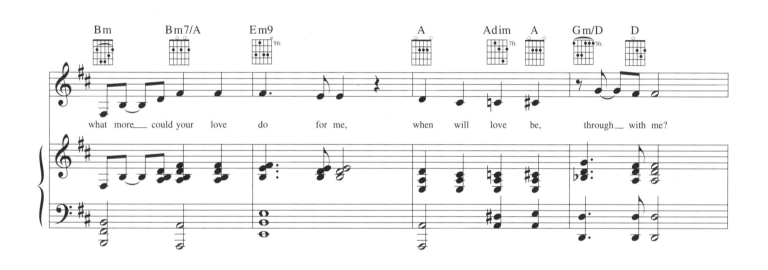

what more ___ could your love do for me, when will love be, through ___ with me?

Why live life from dream to dream, and dread the day, when

dream - - ing   ends.

One day I'll fly___ a - way___   leave all this to

precious illusions

Words & Music by Alanis Morissette

You'll res - cue me right? In the ex - act same__ __ way they__ nev - er did.__ I'll be hap - py right? When your heal - ing powers__ kick__ in.__

Coda

(2° see block chorus, 3° Instrumental)

- ions in my head did not let me down when I was de - fence - less. and part - ing with them is like part - ing with in - vi - si - ble best friend.

These pre - cious il - lu -

Verse 2:
This ring will help me yet
As will you, knight in shining armour
This pill will help me yet
As will these boys gone through like water.

2° & ***D$.***

But this won't work as well as the way it once did
'Cause I want to decide between survival and bliss
And though I know who I'm not I still don't know who I am
But I know I won't keep on playing the victim

Chorus 2:
These precious illusions in my head
Did not let me down when I was a kid
And parting with them
Is like parting with a childhood best friend.

songbird

Words & Music by Christine McVie

2. To_____ you_____

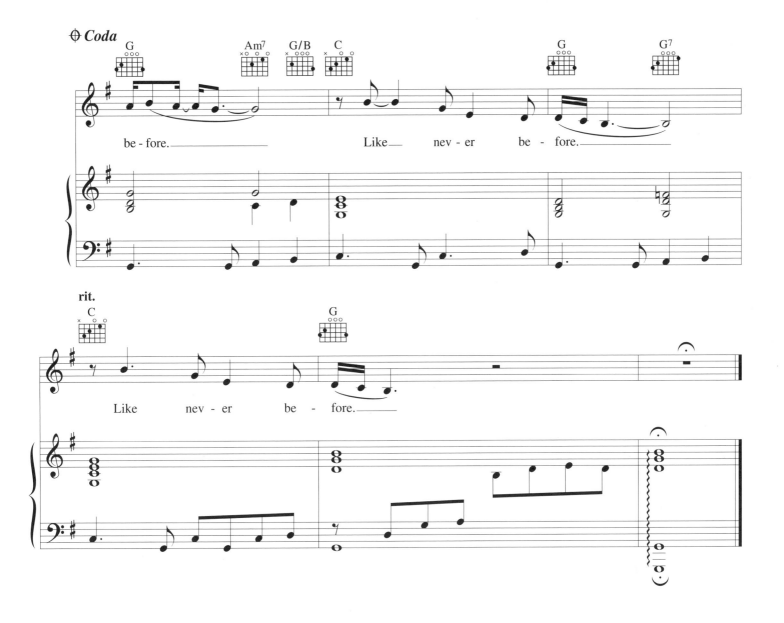

Verse 2:
To you I would give the world
To you I'd never be cold
Cos I feel that when I'm with you
It's alright
I know it's right.

And the songbirds keep singing *etc.*

shoulda woulda coulda

Words & Music by Beverley Knight & Craig Wiseman

1. Peo-ple say that to-geth-er we were both sides_
(Verses 2 & 3 see block lyrics)

of the same coin,_ that we would shine like_ Ve-nus in a clear night

Verse 2:
I could see in the distance all the dreams that were clear to me
And every choice that I had to make left you on your own
Somehow the road we started down had split asunder
Too late to realise how far apart we'd grown.

And how I wish *etc.*

Verse 3:
People ask how it feels to live the kind of life others dream about
I tell them everybody gotta face their highs and their lows
And in my life there's a love that I put aside, 'cause I was busy loving something else
So for every little thing you hold on to, you've got to let something else go.

And how I wish *etc.*

sweet baby

Words by Macy Gray
Music by Joe Solo

Repeat ad lib. to fade

what if

Words & Music by Steve Mac & Wayne Hector

1. Here I stand a-lone_ with_this weight up-on_ my heart_ and it
(Verse 2 see block lyric)

will not go___ a - way.___ In my head I keep_ on look-ing back,_

right back to the start,_ won-drin'_ what it was_ that made you change. Well I

tried but I had to draw____ the line.____ And still this

ques - tion keeps on spin - ning in____ my mind.__ What if

I had nev - er let you go?_____ Would you be the man I used to know?_

What if I had nev - er walked a - way?_____ 'Cause I still

love_ you more that I can say.__ If I'd stayed, if you'd tried,_ if we could on-

- ly turn_ back time._ But I guess we'll nev - er know._

rit.

__ We'll nev - er know. __

Verse 2:
Many roads to take
Some to joy some to heartache
Anyone can lose their way
And if I said that we could turn it back
Right back to the start
Would you take the chance
And make the change?
Do you think how it would have been sometimes
Do you pray that I'd never left your side.

What if I had never let you go? *etc.*

a thousand miles

Words & Music by Vanessa Carlton

1. Mak-ing my way down town, walk-ing fast;
(Verse 2 see block lyric)

— fac-es pass, and I'm home-bound.

Verse 2:
It's always times like these
When I think of you
And I wonder if you ever think of me
'Cause everything's so wrong
And I don't belong
Living in your precious memory
'Cause I need you
And I miss you
And now I wonder:

If I could fall into the sky *etc.*

underneath your clothes

Words by Shakira
Music by Shakira & Lester Mendez

like a la-dy tied to her man-ners, I'm tied up to this feel - ing.

- ing.

Un - der - neath your clothes there's an end - less sto - ry,

there's the man I chose,___ there's my ter-ri-to-ry, and
all the things I de-serve,___ for be-ing such a good_ girl, ho-ney.___

1. be-ing such a good_ girl,

2. for be-ing such a good_ girl.___

molto rall.

Verse 2:
Because of you
I forgot the smart ways to lie
Because of you
I'm running out of reasons to cry
When the friends are gone
When the party's over
We will still belong to each other.

wise up

Words & Music by Aimee Mann

It's ___ not ___ (Verse 2 see block lyric) what you ___ thought ___

when you first ___ be - gan ___ it. ___ You ___ got what you ___

want,_____ now you can hard - - ly stand_____

_____ it, though_____ by now_____ you know_____ it's not_____ go - ing_____ to stop,_____

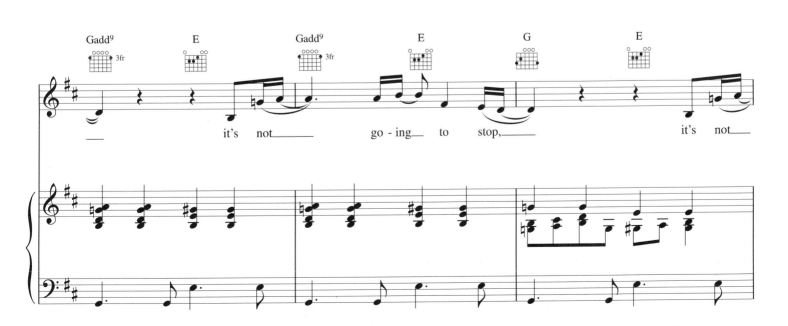

_____ it's not_____ go - ing_____ to stop,_____ it's not_____

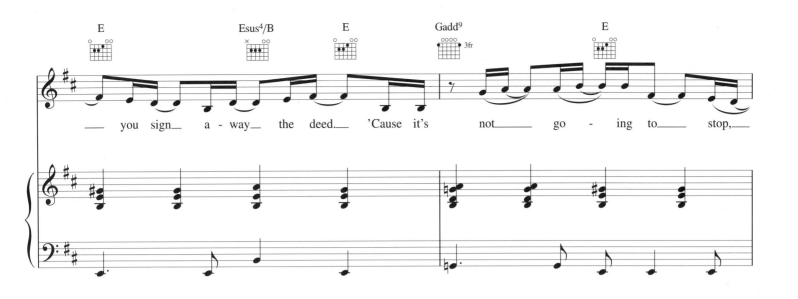

No, it's not go-ing to stop, so just give up.

Repeat to fade

Verse 2:
You're sure there's a cure
And you have finally found it.
You think one drink will shrink you till
You're underground and living down.
But it's not going to stop
It's not going to stop
It's not going to stop
Till you wise up.

1/03 (46345)